Can I Have a Pet?

by Gwendolyn Hudson Hooks • illustrated by Lisa Cinelli

Bebop Books

An imprint of LEE & LOW BOOKS Inc.

Can I have a pet?

Can I have a monkey?

Can I have a tiger?

Can I have a zebra?

Can I have a bear?

Can I have a lion?

Can I have a fish? Yes!